The Camping Trip

By Kirstie Grainger
Illustrated by Steve Cox

OXFORD

UNIVERSITY PRESS

Before you read, can you match the words with the pictures?

1 camping site

2 tent

3 sleeping bag

4 ice cream

5 car

6 beach

7 fire

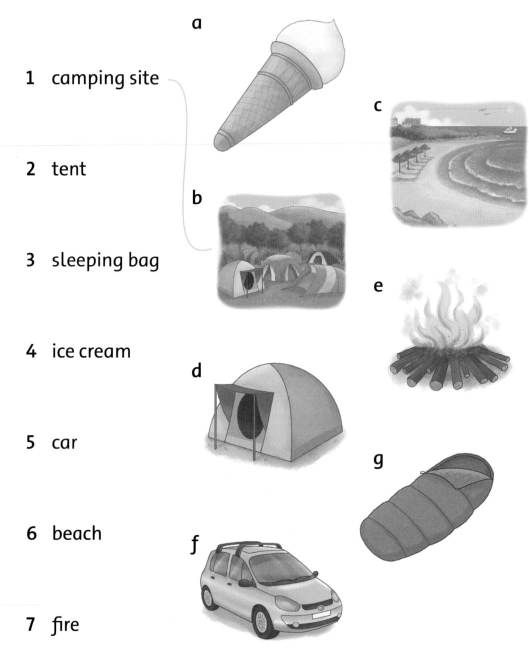

THIS is Anna. She's seven.

Today she is at home with her family.

It's the school holidays.

'I'm bored,' says Anna.

'I'm bored, too,' says Tom.

Tom is Anna's little brother. He's five.

'Mum, we're bored!' says Anna.

'What can we do?'

bored

'Let's go camping,' says Mum.
'Good idea!' says Dad.

They look at a map.
'Look,' says Mum. 'There's a camping site in Upton.
It's near the beach.'
'Great!' says Dad. 'Let's go there.'

beach   camping   camping site   map

They look for the camping things.
'Where's my sleeping bag?' asks Tom.
'It's in the cupboard,' says Mum.
'Where's my sleeping mat?' asks Anna.
'It's under your bed,' says Mum.
'Where's the camping stove?' asks Dad.
'It's in this drawer,' says Mum.

camping stove

cupboard

sleeping bag

sleeping mat

'Where's the tent?' asks Dad.

'I don't know,' says Mum.

They look upstairs. They look downstairs.

They look everywhere.

Mum finds the tent under the stairs.

'Here it is!' she says.

stairs

tent

Dad finds some chairs and blankets. Mum puts some food in a bag. Anna and Tom put some clothes in a bag. Dad puts lots of things in the car. He puts some things on the roof.

'Wait!' says Tom. 'I haven't got my teddy!'
He finds his teddy.
Now they are ready. Off they go!

blanket	car	roof	teddy

What do they say?

a I haven't got my teddy!
b ~~Mum, we're bored!~~
c Let's go camping.
d Where's the tent?
e There's a camping site in Upton.

Write the words.

drawer   chair   ~~teddy~~

stairs   tent   roof

cupboard

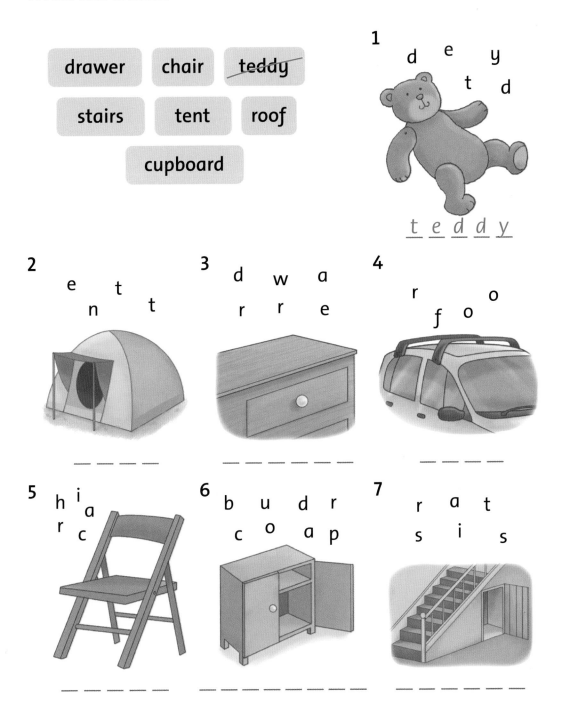

1

d   e   y

t   d

t e d d y

2

e   t
n   t

_ _ _ _

3

d   w   a
r   r   e

_ _ _ _ _ _

4

r   o
f   o

_ _ _ _

5

h i
r   a
  c

_ _ _ _ _

6

b   u   d   r
c   o   a   p

_ _ _ _ _ _ _

7

r   a   t
s   i   s

_ _ _ _ _ _

7

They drive and drive and drive. It's a long way!
Tom and Anna play games in the car.
They count the red cars.
They count the blue cars.
'I'm hungry!' says Tom.

count	drive	hungry

'Let's have a picnic,' says Mum.
They find a park and get out of the car.

Mum finds the food. Dad makes some sandwiches.
'Cheese, please,' says Anna.
'Chicken and cheese and salad, please,' says Tom.
Tom's sandwich is big!

park

picnic

sandwich

They get into the car. They drive and drive and drive.
They see houses and shops.
They see cows and sheep.
'I'm bored!' says Anna.

'Let's listen to music,' says Tom.
'Good idea!' says Anna.

cow  house sheep shop

They arrive in Upton.
'Here's the camping site!' says Mum.

It's sunny. The camping site is very nice.
Tom and Anna are happy.
'I can see the sea!' says Anna.
Dad looks at the roof. 'Oh, no!' he says.
'Where's the tent? It was on the roof!'

sea

sunny

Match the sentences with the pictures.

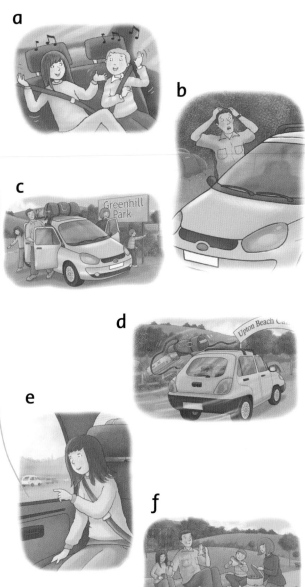

1 Anna plays games in the car.

2 They find a park.

3 They have a picnic.

4 They listen to music.

5 They arrive at the camping site.

6 Dad looks at the roof.

Write the words.

happy	hungry	bored	nice	big

1 Tom is ___hungry___.

2 Tom's sandwich is _____.

3 Anna is _____.

4 The camping site is very _____.

5 Tom and Anna are _____.

'Let's find the tent,' says Dad.

'It's late,' says Mum. 'It's seven o'clock!'

'But where can we sleep?' asks Anna.

'I know,' says Dad. 'Let's make a shelter.'

'A shelter?' says Tom. 'What's that?'

'Look,' says Dad.

Dad makes a shelter with sticks, stones and leaves.

Anna, Tom and Mum help him.

'This is a great shelter!' says Tom.

'We can look for the tent tomorrow,' says Mum.

leaves	shelter	sticks	stones

'Let's have dinner,' says Dad. 'We've got rice and fish.'

'Great!' says Tom. 'I like fish.'

'And I like rice,' says Anna.

'Where's the camping stove?' asks Mum.

'Oh, dear!' says Dad. 'It was on the roof!'

'Let's make a fire,' says Anna.

fire

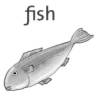
fish

rice

Anna and Tom make a fire. Mum helps them.
Then Dad cooks the rice and fish on the fire.
'Yum!' says Tom. 'I'm not hungry now!'
'It's nine o'clock,' says Mum. 'It's time to go to bed.'
'I'm tired,' says Tom.

tired

Tom and Anna put their sleeping mats and
their sleeping bags in the shelter.
'This is my bed,' says Tom.
'And this is my bed,' says Anna. 'I like my bed!'
They put on their pyjamas and go to bed.

'Oh no, it's raining!' says Anna.
But it's OK. It's wet outside, but it's dry in the shelter.

pyjamas

raining

Circle the correct words.

1 They make a shelter / house with sticks, stones and leaves.

2 Anna likes / doesn't like rice.

3 Mum / Dad helps Anna and Tom to make a fire.

4 Dad cooks dinner on the camping stove / fire .

5 They have rice and chicken / rice and fish for dinner.

6 Tom and Anna go to bed in their sleeping bags / car .

7 It's wet / dry outside the shelter.

8 Tom and Anna go to bed at eight o'clock / nine o'clock .

Write the words.

fish   fire   tired   ~~shelter~~   stove   dry

1 This is a great _shelter!_

2 I like _____.

3 Where's the camping _____ ?

4 Let's make a _____.

5 I'm _____.

6 It's _____ in the shelter.

It's morning. It's sunny. Tom and Anna put on shorts and T-shirts.

'Let's go outside,' says Anna.

They see a family – a boy, a man and a woman.

They have got a big tent.

The boy sees Anna and Tom. He comes to their shelter.

'Hello,' he says. 'I'm Sam.'

'Hello, Sam,' says Anna. 'I'm Anna. And this is Tom.'

shorts   T-shirt

'Look,' says Sam. 'That's our tent.'
'We haven't got a tent,' says Tom. 'We've got
a shelter! It's made of sticks, stones and leaves.'
'Wow! Can I look inside?' asks Sam.

The children go into the shelter.
'This is our bedroom,' says Anna.
'It's a great shelter!' says Sam.

'Look, Mum and Dad,' says Anna. 'We've got a new friend! His name is Sam.'
'Look, Mum and Dad,' says Sam. 'I've got two new friends! Their names are Anna and Tom.'

The mums and dads say hello.
'What's that?' asks Anna.
'It's a tent,' says Sam's dad. 'It was on the road!'
'That's our tent!' says Dad.

friends   road

'And what's that?' asks Tom.

'It's a camping stove,' says Sam's mum. 'It was on the road, too!'

'That's our camping stove!' says Mum.

'A shelter is fun,' says Tom. 'A shelter is better than a tent!'

'And a fire is better than a camping stove!' says Anna.

fun

Tom and Anna play with Sam. They play football. They climb trees. They play in the shelter. They make sandcastles on the beach. They eat ice creams. They make dinner on the fire.

They stay for two days. Then it's time to go home. 'That was a great holiday!' says Anna.

football

ice cream

sandcastle

tree

Tick (✔) the correct words.

1 In the morning it's ...

   a [✔] sunny.   b [ ] raining.

2 Sam is camping with his mum and ...

   a [ ] brother.   b [ ] dad.

3 The shelter is made of stones, sticks and ...

   a [ ] blankets.   b [ ] leaves.

4 Sam says the shelter is ...

   a [ ] boring   b [ ] great

5 Sam's family find a tent ...

   a [ ] in the sea.   b [ ] on the road.

6 They make sandcastles and eat ...

   a [ ] ice cream.   b [ ] sandwiches.

7 Anna and Tom stay at the camping site for ...

   a [ ] two days.   b [ ] three days.

Crossword.

sunny   friend   football   sea

~~sandcastle~~   ice cream   tree   road

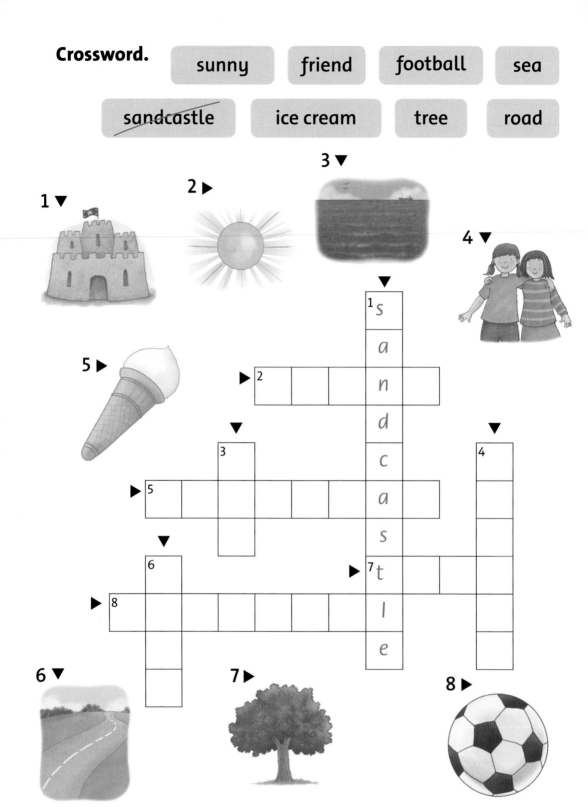

Find the things in the room. Then write the words.

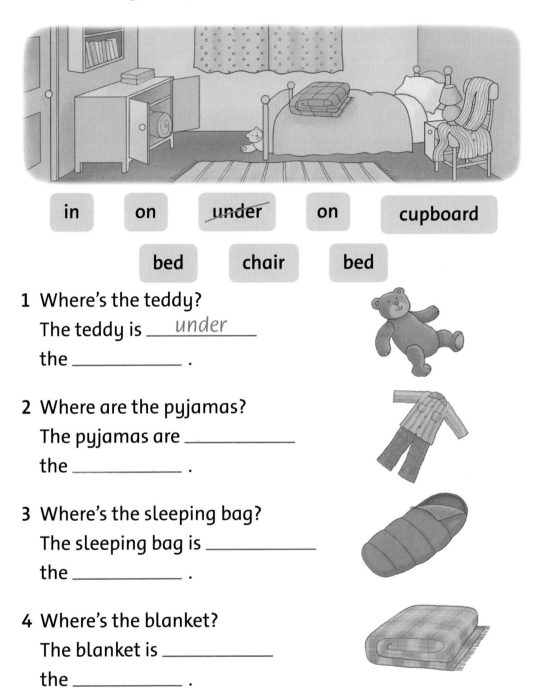

in	on	~~under~~	on	cupboard

bed	chair	bed

1 Where's the teddy?
   The teddy is ____under____
   the _____ .

2 Where are the pyjamas?
   The pyjamas are _____
   the _____ .

3 Where's the sleeping bag?
   The sleeping bag is _____
   the _____ .

4 Where's the blanket?
   The blanket is _____
   the _____ .

**Play the speaking game. Add new words each time.
How many can you remember?**

I'm going camping.
I've got a tent.

I'm going camping.
I've got a tent and
a sleeping mat.

I'm going camping.
I've got a tent and a sleeping
mat and two T-shirts.

Design a shelter. Use these things. Draw your shelter and talk about it

This is my shelter. It's made of a table, a blanket and three chairs.

This is my shelter ...

OXFORD
UNIVERSITY PRESS

Great Clarendon Street, Oxford OX2 6DP

Oxford University Press is a department of the University of Oxford.
It furthers the University's objective of excellence in research, scholarship,
and education by publishing worldwide in

Oxford New York

Auckland Cape Town Dar es Salaam Hong Kong Karachi
Kuala Lumpur Madrid Melbourne Mexico City Nairobi
New Delhi Shanghai Taipei Toronto

With offices in

Argentina Austria Brazil Chile Czech Republic France Greece
Guatemala Hungary Italy Japan Poland Portugal Singapore
South Korea Switzerland Thailand Turkey Ukraine Vietnam

OXFORD and OXFORD ENGLISH are registered trade marks of
Oxford University Press in the UK and in certain other countries

ISBN: 978 0 19 480258 1

Printed in China

ACKNOWLEDGEMENTS
Story by: Kirstie Grainger
Illustrated by: Steve Cox